Christmas hits

For SATB Choir With Piano Accompaniment

Arranged by Berty Rice

Cover design by Miranda Harvey
Printed in the United Kingdom by Caligraving Limited, Thetford, Norfolk

Novello Publishing Limited
8-9 Frith Street London W1D 3JB

Happy Xmas (War Is Over)

Words and Music by John Lennon & Yoko Ono

7
Alto
fun, The near and the dear ones, The old and the
Em B/E B7/E Em A7sus4 A7 G/A A7
9
Soprano
mf
A mer-ry, mer-ry Christ-mas, and a hap-py new
Alto
young.
D A/D A7/D D G
mf
11
Soprano
year, let's hope it's a good one, with-out a-ny
A Em G6

13
Soprano
fears.
War is o - ver
Alto
War is o - ver
Tenor
And so this is Christ-mas; for weak and for
D D/E A E/A E7/A A
15
if you want it, War is o - ver
if you want it, War is o - ver
strong, the rich and the poor ones, the road is so
Bm F♯/B F7/B Bm E7sus4 E7 D/E E7

17
mp
now.
War is o - ver
mp
now.
War is o - ver
long.
f
And so hap-py Christ-mas
For black and for
A E/A E7/A A D A/D A7/D D
mf
19
if you want it, war is o - ver
if you want it, war is o - ver
white, For the yel-low and red ones,
Let's stop all the
Em B/E B7/E Em A7sus4 G/A A7

21
f
now. Mer-ry Christ - mas, and a hap-py new
f
now. Mer-ry Christ - mas, and a hap-py new
f
A mer-ry, mer-ry Christ - mas, and a hap-py new
f
fights. A mer-ry, mer-ry Christ - mas, and a hap-py new
A A/D A7/D D G
f
23
year, let's hope it's a good one, with-out a - ny
year, let's hope it's a good one, with-out a - ny
year, let's hope it's a good one, with-out a - ny
year, let's hope it's a good one, with-out a - ny
A Em G6

25
fears.
mf
fears.
And so this is Christ-mas,
And what have we
p
fears.
War is o - ver
p
fears.
War is o - ver
D
D/A
A
E/A
Bm/A
A
dim.
mp
27
done?
An-oth-er year o-ver,
A new one just be-
if you want it, War is o - ver
if you want it, War is o - ver
Bm/A
F♯7/A
Bm/A
Bm7/A
E7/A
Bm/A
E7/A

29
f
And so hap-py Christ-mas, We hope you have
- gun.
mp
now. War is o - ver
mp
now. War is o - ver
A E/A G/A A7 D A/D Em/D D
mf
31
fun, The near and the dear ones, The old and the
if you want it, war is o - ver
if you want it, war is o - ver
Em/D B7/D Em/D Em7/D A7/D Em/D A7/D

33
f
young,
A mer-ry, mer-ry Christ-mas,
and a hap-py new
A mer-ry, mer-ry Christ-mas,
and a hap-py new
now.
Mer-ry Christ-mas,
and a hap-py new
now.
Mer-ry Christ-mas,
and a hap-py new
D
A7/D
C/D
D7
G
35
year,
let's hope it's a
good one,
with-out a-ny
year,
let's hope it's a
good one,
with-out a-ny
year,
let's hope it's a
good one,
with-out a-ny
year,
let's hope it's a
good one,
with-out a-ny
A
E dim
Em7(♭5)/G
A7(♭9)

37
fears.
War is o - ver,
fears.
War is o - ver,
fears.
War is o - ver,
fears.
War is o - ver,
D Bm7 E7 A E/A E7/A A
39
if you want it, war is o - ver,
if you want it, war is o - ver,
if you want it, war is o - ver,
if you want it, war is o - ver,
Bm/A F#7/A Bm/A Bm7/A E7/A D/A E7/A

41
dim. e rit al fine
now. War is o - ver,
dim. e rit al fine
now. War is o - ver,
dim. e rit al fine
now. War is o - ver,
dim. e rit al fine
now. War is o - ver,
A E/A E7/A A F♯m7 E/F♯ E7/F♯ F♯m7
dim. e rit al fine
43
if you want it, war is o - ver now.
if you want it, war is o - ver now.
if you want it, war is o - ver now.
if you want it, war is o - ver now.
Bm F♯7/B Bm Bm7/E E7 D/E E7 A

Keeping The Dream Alive

Words & Music Zauner/Strobel/Touchton/Briggs

8
And while the past is call - ing, in my fan - ta - sy I re -
And while the past is call - ing, in my fan - ta - sy I re -
E F♯m6 F♯m7 Edim7/G E/G♯♯ F♯7/A♯ A6
11
mf
The hopes we had were much too high,
mf
The hopes we had were much too high,
mf
-mem-ber their fa - ces. The hopes we had were much too high,
mf
-mem-ber their fa - ces. The hopes we had were much too high,
E/G♯ A/B E mf E7
f

14
Way out of reach, but we had to try.
Way out of reach, but we had to try.
Way out of reach, but we had to try. The game will ne-ver be o
Way out of reach, but we had to try. The game will ne-ver be o
f
f
A/E
Am7/D
E
D♯dim/F♯
17
- ver, Be-cause we're keep - ing the dream a - live.
- ver, Be-cause we're keep - ing the dream a - live.
A
E/B
B13sus4
F♯m7/B
E

20
mp
I hear my-self re - call - ing Things you said to me The
mp
I hear my-self re - call - ing Things you said to me The
p
doo doo doo doo doo doo doo doo doo doo doo doo
p
doo doo doo doo doo doo doo doo doo doo doo doo
23
night it all start - ed. And still the rain is fall - ing; Makes me
night it all start - ed. And still the rain is fall - ing; Makes me
doo doo doo doo doo doo doo doo doo doo doo doo
doo doo doo doo doo doo doo doo doo doo doo doo

26
mf
feel the way I felt when we part - ed The hopes we had
mf
feel the way I felt when we part - ed The hopes we had
mp
doo doo doo doo doo doo doo doo doo doo doo doo
mp
doo doo doo doo doo doo doo doo doo doo doo doo

29
were much too high, Way out of reach, but we had to try.
were much too high, Way out of reach, but we had to try.
doo doo doo doo doo doo doo doo doo doo doo doo
doo doo doo doo doo doo doo doo doo doo doo doo

32
f
No need to hide, no need to run, 'cos all the an-
f
No need to hide, no need to run, 'cos all the an-
mf
doo doo doo doo doo doo doo doo doo doo doo doo
mf
doo doo doo doo doo doo doo doo doo doo doo doo
E
E7
A/E
mf
35
f
- swers come one by one. The game will ne - ver be o -
f
- swers come one by one. The game will ne - ver be o -
f
doo doo doo doo The game will ne - ver be o -
f
doo doo doo doo The game will ne - ver be o -
Am7/D
E
D♯dim7/F♯
f

37
ver, Be- cause we're keep-ing the dream a - live.
ver, Be- cause we're keep-ing the dream a - live.
ver, Be- cause we're keep-ing the dream a - live.
mp
ver, Be- cause we're keep-ing the dream a - live. I need
A E/B B13sus4 F♯m7/B E
dim.
40
p
cresc.
ooh
cresc.
I love you.
p
cresc.
ooh I love you.
cresc.
you I love you.
F♯m7 G♯m7 Amaj7 G♯ B7
cresc.

44
f
The game will ne - ver be o - ver, Be - cause we're
E
D♯dim/F♯
A
E/B
46
keep - ing the dream a - live. The hopes we had were much too high,
B13sus4
F♯m7/B
E
E7

49
Way out of reach, but we had to try. No need to hide,
A/E
D7
E
52
no need to run, 'cos all the an - swers come one by one.
E7
A/E
D9

55
The hopes we had were much too high, Way out of reach,
The hopes we had were much too high, Way out of reach,
doo doo doo doo doo doo doo doo doo doo doo
doo doo doo doo doo doo doo doo doo doo doo
E
58
but we had to try. No need to hide, no need to run,
but we had to try. No need to hide, no need to run,
doo doo doo doo doo doo doo doo doo doo doo doo
doo doo doo doo doo doo doo doo doo doo doo doo
E
E7/D

61
'cos all the an - swers come one by one.
'cos all the an - swers come one by one.
doo doo doo doo doo doo doo doo
doo doo doo doo doo doo doo doo
A/C♯
D7sus4/C
D7/C
63
The game will ne - ver be o - ver, Be - cause we're
The game will ne - ver be o - ver, Be - cause we're
The game will ne - ver be o - ver, Be - cause we're
The game will ne - ver be o - ver, Be - cause we're
E/B
Bmaj7(♭6)
F♯m7/B
Emaj7/B

65
ff
keep-ing the dream a-live.
The game will ne-ver be o-
B13sus4
F♯m7/B
E/B
F♯m7/B
E
D♯(♯9)/A♯
68
rit.
ver, Be-cause we're keep-ing the dream a-live.
F♯m7/A
Amaj11/C♯
F♯m13
F♯m7/B
E

Mistletoe And Wine

Words by Leslie Stewart & Jeremy Paul
Music by Keith Strachan

18
Soprano
Alto
Tenor
king, the ca - rol - lers sing, The old is past, it's a
Bass
mp
The old is past, it's a
Gm
23
mp
Dreams of San - ta, dreams of
new be - gin-ning.
new be - gin-ning.
F
E♭
B♭/D

28
cresc.
mf
snow, fin - gers numb, fa - ces a - glow. It's Christ - mas -
mp
fin - gers numb, fa - ces a - glow. It's Christ - mas -
fa - ces a - glow. It's
B♭6/D B♭/C C7 F7 E♭/F F7 F9 B♭

34
time, Mis - tle - toe and wine, Chil - dren sing - ing
Christ - mas - time, Mis - tle - toe and wine, Chil - dren
E♭/B♭

39
Chris - ti - an rhyme, With logs on the fi - re and gifts on the
Chris - ti - an rhyme, With logs on the fi - re and gifts on the
sing - ing Chris - ti - an rhyme, With logs on the fi - re and
sing - ing Chris - ti - an rhyme, With logs on the fi - re and
F9 B♭6/F F9 B♭/F F7 Cm/F F7sus4 F7 F7sus4 F7 Cm9/F
44
tree, A time to re - joice in the good that we see. A
tree, A time to re - joice in the good that we see.
gifts on the tree, A time to re - joice in the good that we
gifts on the tree, A time to re - joice in the good that we
F7 B♭/F F F13 Cm/F B♭6 B♭ B♭sus4 B♭

49
time for liv-ing, a time for be-liev-ing, A time for
A time for
see.
see.
B♭
Gm
54
trust-ing, not de-ceiv-ing.
trust-ing, not de-ceiv-ing.
Love and laugh-ter and joy e-ver
F
E♭
B♭/D

60
Ours for the tak-ing, just fol-low the mas-ter.
Ours for the tak-ing, just fol-low the mas-ter.
af-ter, Ours for the tak-ing, just fol-low the mas-ter.
Ours for the tak-ing, just fol-low the mas-ter.
B♭6/D
B♭/C
C7
E♭/F
F7
65
f
Christ-mas-time, Mis-tle-toe and wine, Child-ren
Christ-mas-time, Mis-tle-toe and wine, Child-ren
Christ-mas-time, Mis-tle-toe and wine,
Christ-mas-time, Mis-tle-toe and wine,
B♭

70
sing - ing Chris - ti - an rhyme, With logs on the fi - re and gifts on the
sing - ing Chris - ti - an rhyme, With logs on the fi - re and gifts on the
Child - ren sing - ing Chris - ti - an rhyme, With logs on the fi - re and
Child - ren sing - ing Chris - ti - an rhyme, With logs on the fi - re and

76
mp
tree, A time to re - joice in the good that we see. A
tree, A time to re - joice in the good that we see.
gifts on the tree, A time to re - joice in the good that we
gifts on the tree, A time to re - joice in the good that we
N.C.
B♭
B♭sus4
B♭
mp

81
time___ for giv-ing, a time for for - get - ting, a time for for -
A time for for -
see.
see.
B♭
Gm
86
molto cresc.
giv-ing and for for - get - ting. Christ-mas is love, Christ-mas is
giv-ing and for for - get - ting. Christ-mas is love, Christ-mas is
and for for - get - ting. Christ-mas is love, Christ-mas is
Christ-mas is love, Christ-mas is
F
E♭
Am7(♭5)
D7 Cadd9 F♯dim7
molto cresc.

92
molto f
peace; A time for hat - ing and fight-ing to cease. Christ - mas -
molto f
peace; A time for hat - ing and fight-ing to cease. Christ - mas -
peace; A time for hat - ing and fight-ing to cease.
peace; A time for hat - ing and fight-ing to cease.
Gm9 Gm
N.C.
B♭
molto f

98
time, Mis-tle-toe and wine, Child - ren sing - ing
time, Mis-tle-toe and wine, Child - ren sing - ing
molto f
Christ - mas - time, Mis-tle-toe and wine, Child - ren
molto f
Christ - mas - time, Mis-tle-toe and wine, Child - ren
E♭/B♭

103
Chris - ti - an rhyme, With logs on the fi - re and gifts on the
Chris - ti - an rhyme, With logs on the fi - re and gifts on the
sing - ing Chris - ti - an rhyme, With logs on the fi - re and
sing - ing Chris - ti - an rhyme, With logs on the fi - re and
F9 B♭6/F F9 B♭/F F7 Cm/F F7sus4 F7 F7sus4 F7 Cm9/F
108
rit.
tree, a time to re - joice in the good that we see.
rit.
tree, a time to re - joice in the good that we see.
rit.
gifts on the tree, re - joice in the good that we see.
rit.
gifts on the tree, re - joice in the good that we see.
F7 B♭/F F F13 Cm/F Am7(♭5) B♭ F7sus4 B♭
rit.

Merry Xmas Everybody

Words & Music by Neville Holder & James Lea

9
that ev' - ry San - ta has a ball.
Does he ride
Does he ride
D
Bm7
F♯m7
A
E7sus4/B
A7/C♯
Em7/B
A7
13
a red - nosed rein - deer? Has a ton up - on his sleigh?
a red - nosed rein - deer? Has a ton up - on his sleigh?
G
D
G

16
mf
Do the fai - ries keep him so - ber for a day?
mf
Do the fai - ries keep him so - ber for a day?
Do the fai - ries keep him so - ber for a day?
Do the fai - ries keep him so - ber for a day?
D Adim7/D♯ Em7 Em/D A7/C♯ Em7/B A E7sus4/B
cresc.
20
f
So here it is: Mer-ry Christ - mas, ev' - ry-bo - dy's hav-ing fun.
f
So here it is: Mer-ry Christ - mas, ev' - ry-bo - dy's hav-ing fun.
f
So here it is: Mer-ry Christ - mas, ev' - ry-bo - dy's hav-ing fun.
f
So here it is: Mer-ry Christ - mas, ev' - ry-bo - dy's hav-ing fun.
A7/C♯ Em7/B A7 D Bm7 F♯m7 Dm7/F
f

24
Look to the fu - ture now, it's on - ly just be -
Look to the fu - ture now, it's on - ly just be -
Look to the fu - ture now, it's on - ly just be -
Look to the fu - ture now, it's on - ly just be -
A7/E A7 D Bm7 F♯m7 F
28
- gun.
mf
- gun. Are you wait - ing for the fam -
- gun.
- gun.
A7 A7/G D/F♯ A7/E D Bm7
dim.
mp

32
mf
Are you sure you got the room
- 'ly to ar - rive?
F♯m7
A
E7sus4/B
A7/C♯
Em7/B
A7
D
Bm7
36
to spare in - side?
Does your Gran - ny al - ways tell
Does your Gran - ny al - ways tell
F♯m7
A
E7sus4/B
A7/C♯
Em7/B
A7
G

40
you that the old songs are the best? Then she's up
you that the old songs are the best? Then she's up
mf
Then she's up
mf
Then she's up
D
G
D
Adim7/D♯
43
and rock 'n' roll - in' with the best.
and rock 'n' roll - in' with the best.
and rock 'n' roll - in' with the best.
and rock 'n' roll - in' with the best.
Em7
Em/D
A7/C♯
Em7/B
A
E7sus4/B
cresc.

46
f
So here it is: Mer-ry Christ - mas, ev' - ry - bo - dy's hav - ing fu
f
So here it is: Mer-ry Christ - mas, ev' - ry - bo - dy's hav - ing fu
f
So here it is: Mer-ry Christ - mas, ev' - ry - bo - dy's hav - ing fu
f
So here it is: Mer-ry Christ - mas, ev' - ry - bo - dy's hav - ing fu
A7/C♯ Em7/B A7 D Bm7 F♯m7 Dm/F
f
50
dim.
— Look to the fu - ture now, — it's on - ly just be - gun. —
dim.
— Look — to the fu - ture now, — it's on - ly just be - gun. —
dim.
— Look — to the fu - ture now, — it's on - ly just be - gun. —
dim.
— Look to the fu - ture now, — it's on - ly just be - gun.
A7/E A7/E D Bm7 F♯m7 F

55
p
What will your dad - dy do when he sees your ma - ma kis - sing San -
cresc.
What will your dad - dy do when he sees your ma - ma kis - sing San -
What will your dad - dy do when he sees your ma - ma kis - sing San -
What will your dad - dy do when he sees your ma - ma kis - sing San -
58
- ta Claus? A - ha!
f
Are you hang - ing up a stock -
- ta Claus? A - ha!
- ta Claus? A - ha!
Are you hang - ing up a stock -
N.C.
A7/E
A7
D
mp
cresc.
f

62
f
Are you hop - ing that the snow
- ing on your wall?
f
Are you hop - ing that the snow
- ing on your wall?
F♯m7
A
E7sus4/B
A7/C♯
Em7/B
A7
D
Bm7
66
- will start to fall?
Do you ride
Do you ride
- will start to fall?
Do you ride
Do you ride
F♯m7
A
E7sus4/B
A7/C♯
Em7/B
A7

69
— on down — the hill - side in a bug - gy you — have made? —
— on down — the hill - side in a bug - gy you — have made? —
— on down — the hill - side in a bug - gy you — have made? —
— on down — the hill - side in a bug - gy you — have made? —
G D G
72
— When you land — u - pon — your head — then you — been slayed! —
— When you land — u - pon — your head — then you — been slayed! —
— When you land — u - pon — your head — then you — been slayed! —
— When you land — u - pon — your head — then you — been slayed! —
D Adim7/D♯ Em7 Em/D A7/C♯ Em7/B

75
mp
So here it is: Mer-ry Christ - mas, ev' - ry - bo -
A
E7sus4/B
A7/C♯
79
- dy's hav - ing fun.
Look to the fu - ture now, it's

83
cresc.
f
on - ly just be - gun, it's on - ly just be - gun, so here it
cresc.
f
on - ly just be - gun, it's on - ly just be - gun, so here it
cresc.
f
on - ly just be - gun, it's on - ly just be - gun, so here it
cresc.
f
on - ly just be - gun, it's on - ly just be - gun, so here it
mf
cresc.
87
is, Mer-ry Christ - mas, ev'-ry-bo - dy's hav-ing fun.
is, Mer-ry Christ - mas, ev'-ry-bo - dy's hav-ing fun.
is, Mer-ry Christ - mas, ev'-ry-bo - dy's hav-ing fun.
is, Mer-ry Christ - mas, ev'-ry-bo - dy's hav-ing fun.
E C♯m7 G♯m7 Em7/G B7/F♯ B7
f

91
Look to the fu - ture now, it's on - ly just be - gun, it's
Look to the fu - ture now, it's on - ly just be - gun, it's
Look to the fu - ture now, it's on - ly just be - gun, it's
Look to the fu - ture now, it's on - ly just be - gun, it's
E C♯m7 G♯m7 Em7/A G6
95
on - ly just be - gun, so here it is!
on - ly just be - gun, so here it is!
on - ly just be - gun, so here it is!
on - ly just be - gun, so here it is!
F♯m7 B7 E6

Jingle Bells

Words & Music by J.S. Pierpont

9
mf
Th
cross the fields we go, we're laugh - ing all the way.
A9
C9(♭5)
B9
Em7
Am7
D13
13
mf
Wh
bells on bob - tails ring, they're mak - ing spi - rits bright.
G7
C9
F9
B♭m7(♭5)/E

17
fun it is to ride and sing a sleigh-ing song to - night.
Am7(♭5)/E♭ D6 Am7/D G6/D Am7/D G6/D Am7/D
21
f
Jin - gle bells, jin - gle bells, jin - gle all the way.
f
Jin - gle bells, jin - gle bells, jin - gle all the way.
f
Jin - gle bells, jin - gle bells, jin - gle all the way.
f
Jin - gle bells, jin - gle bells, jin - gle all the way.
G C♯9(♭5) Cmaj7 F9/C Bm7 E7(♯9)
f

25
Oh what fun it is to ride in a one horse o - pen sleigh! Oh
Oh what fun it is to ride in a one horse o - pen sleigh! Oh
Oh what fun it is to ride in a one horse o - pen sleigh! Oh
Oh what fun it is to ride in a one horse o - pen sleigh! Oh
Am7 Cm7 B7(♭9) E7(♭9) Em7/A A13 C/D D aug

29
jin - gle bells, jin - gle bells, jin - gle all the way.
jin - gle bells, jin - gle bells, jin - gle all the way.
jin - gle bells, jin - gle bells, jin - gle all the way.
jin - gle bells, jin - gle bells, jin - gle all the way.
G C♯9(♭5) Cmaj7 F9/C Bm7 E7(♯9)

33
Oh what fun it is to ride in a one horse o - pen sleigh.
Oh what fun it is to ride in a one horse o - pen sleigh.
Oh what fun it is to ride in a one horse o - pen sleigh.
Oh what fun it is to ride in a one horse o - pen sleigh.
Am7 Cm7 B7♭9 E7♭9 Am7 D7(♭9) G6 F13
37
G7 C9 G7 C9
dim.

41
p
Now the ground is white,
go it while you're young,
G7
C9
F9
B♭m7(♭5)/E
45
take the girls to - night
and sing this sleigh-ing song.
Just
cresc.
A9
C9(♭5)
B9
Em7
Am7
D13

49
get a bob - tailed nag, two - for - ty for his speed,
get a bob - tailed nag, two - for - ty for his speed,
get a bob - tailed nag, two - for - ty for his speed,
get a bob - tailed nag, two - for - ty for his speed,
G7 C9 F9 B♭m7♭5/E
53
hitch him to an o - pen sleigh and, crack, you'll take the lead.
hitch him to an o - pen sleigh and, crack, you'll take the lead.
hitch him to an o - pen sleigh and, crack, you'll take the lead.
hitch him to an o - pen sleigh and, crack, you'll take the lead.
Am7♭5/E♭ D6 Am7/D G6D Am7/D G6/D Am7/D

57
mf
Jin - gle bells, jin - gle bells, jin - gle all the way.
mf
Jin - gle bells, jin - gle bells, jin - gle all the way.
mf
Jin - gle bells, jin - gle bells, jin - gle all the way.
mf
Jin - gle bells, jin - gle bells, jin - gle all the way.
G

61
Oh what fun it is to ride in a one horse o - pen sleigh! Oh,
Oh what fun it is to ride in a one horse o - pen sleigh! Oh,
Oh what fun it is to ride in a one horse o - pen sleigh! Oh,
Oh what fun it is to ride in a one horse o - pen sleigh! Oh,

65
cresc.
jin - gle bells, jin - gle bells, jin - gle all the way.
cresc.
jin - gle bells, jin - gle bells, jin - gle all the way.
cresc.
jin - gle bells, jin - gle bells, jin - gle all the way.
cresc.
jin - gle bells, jin - gle bells, jin - gle all the way.
G
C♯9(♭5)
Cmaj7
F9/C
Bm7
E7(♯9)
mf cresc.
69
ff
Oh what fun it is to ride in a one horse o - pen
ff
Oh what fun it is to ride in a one horse o - pen
ff
Oh what fun it is to ride in a one horse o - pen
ff
Oh what fun it is to ride in a one horse o - pen
Am7
Cm7
B7(♭9)
E7(♭9)
Am9
Cmaj7
D aug7
D7(♭9)
ff

73
dim.
sleigh, a one horse sleigh, to ride in
dim.
sleigh, a one horse sleigh, to ride in
dim.
sleigh, a one horse sleigh, to ride in
dim.
sleigh, a one horse sleigh, to ride in
G7 C9 G7 C9
dim.
77
p
one horse o - pen, one horse o - pen sleigh.
p
one horse o - pen, one horse o - pen sleigh.
p
one horse o - pen, one horse o - pen sleigh.
p
one horse o - pen, one horse o - pen sleigh.
G7 C9 F9 G6 C7 G6
p